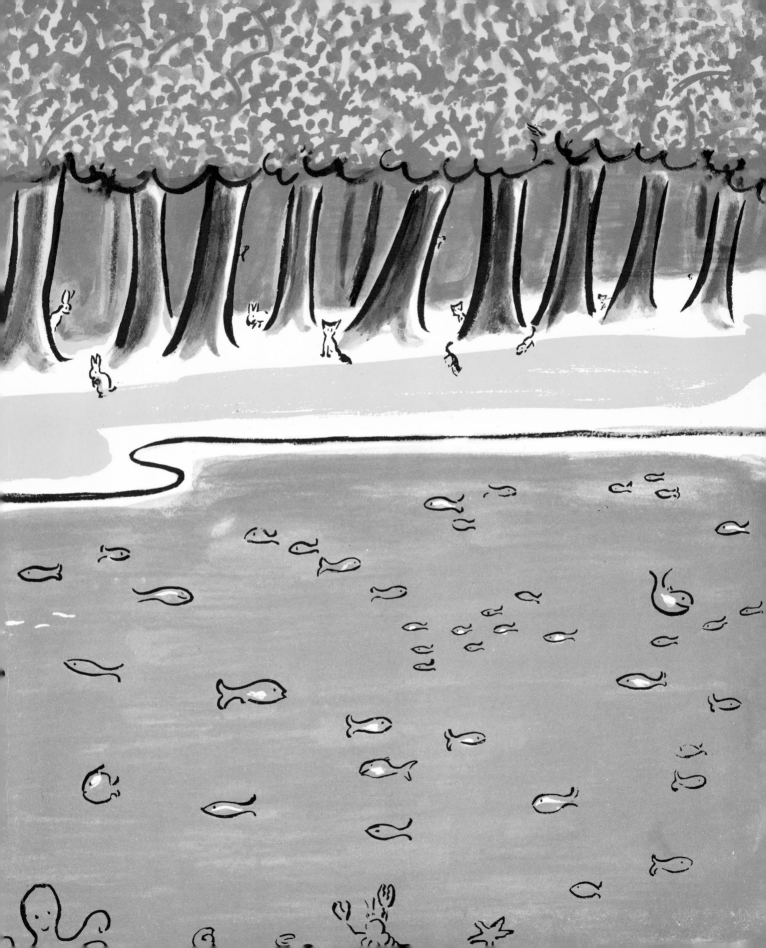

MILLIONS

AND

MILL

BY

LOUIS SLOBODKIN

ONS

AND

MILLIONS!

THE VANGUARD PRESS   NEW YORK

FOR

NATE   &   DAVIE

    &   &

DAVIE   &   NATE

WITH LOVE

THERE ARE MILLIONS AND MILLIONS

AND MILLIONS OF THINGS

AROUND US WHEREVER WE LOOK.

AND SOME OF THOSE MILLIONS

AND MILLIONS OF THINGS

ARE RIGHT HERE IN THIS BOOK!

THERE ARE MILLIONS OF STARS

AND MILLIONS OF CARS

AND MILLIONS OF DOGS

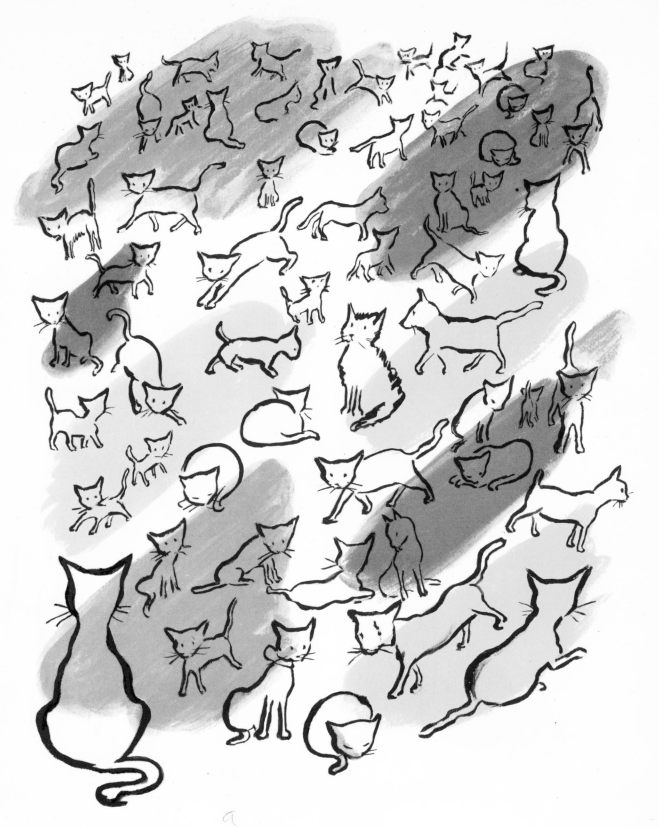

AND CATS.

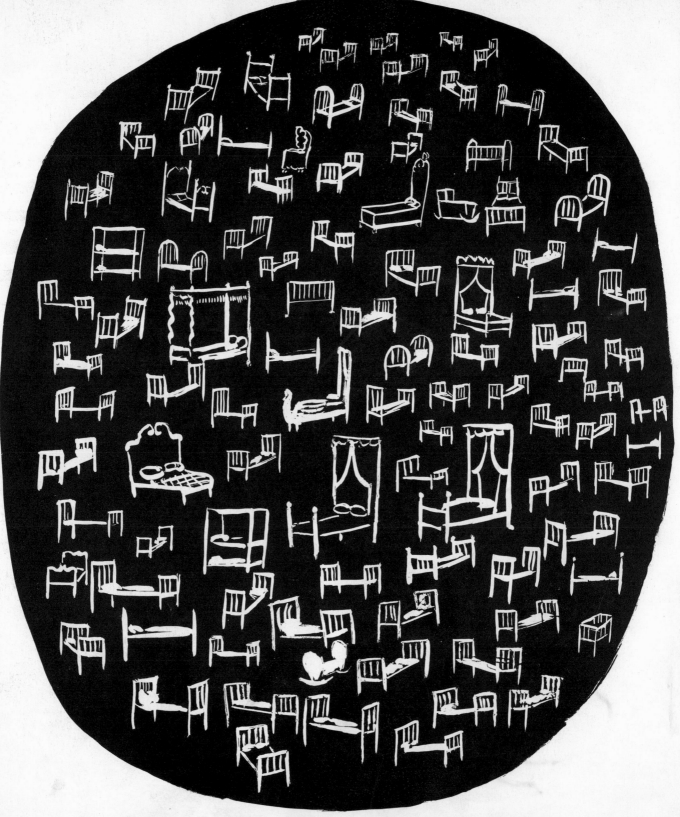

THERE ARE MILLIONS OF BEDS

AND MILLIONS OF HEADS

AND MILLIONS OF BONNETS

AND HATS.

THERE ARE MILLIONS OF SHELLS

AND MILLIONS OF BELLS

AND MILLIONS OF SHIPS AND BOATS.

THERE ARE MILLIONS OF TREES
AND FLOWERS AND BEES

AND MILLIONS OF SNOW-WHITE GOATS.

THERE ARE MILLIONS OF STAIRS
AND MILLIONS OF BEARS

AND MILLIONS OF ICE-CREAM CONES.

THERE ARE MILLIONS OF CLOWNS

AND MILLIONS OF SOUNDS

AND MILLIONS OF TELEPHONES.

THERE ARE MILLIONS OF LAKES
AND DUCKS AND DRAKES

AND MILLIONS AND MILLIONS OF STICKS.

THERE ARE MILLIONS WHO LIVE
BEHIND WALLS OF WOOD

AND MILLIONS WHO LIVE BEHIND BRICKS.

THERE ARE MILLIONS AND MILLIONS
WHO ARE TALL AND THIN

AND MILLIONS WHO ARE SHORT AND ROUND.

THERE ARE MILLIONS WHO FLY
UP HIGH IN THE SKY

AND MILLIONS WHO STAY ON THE GROUND.

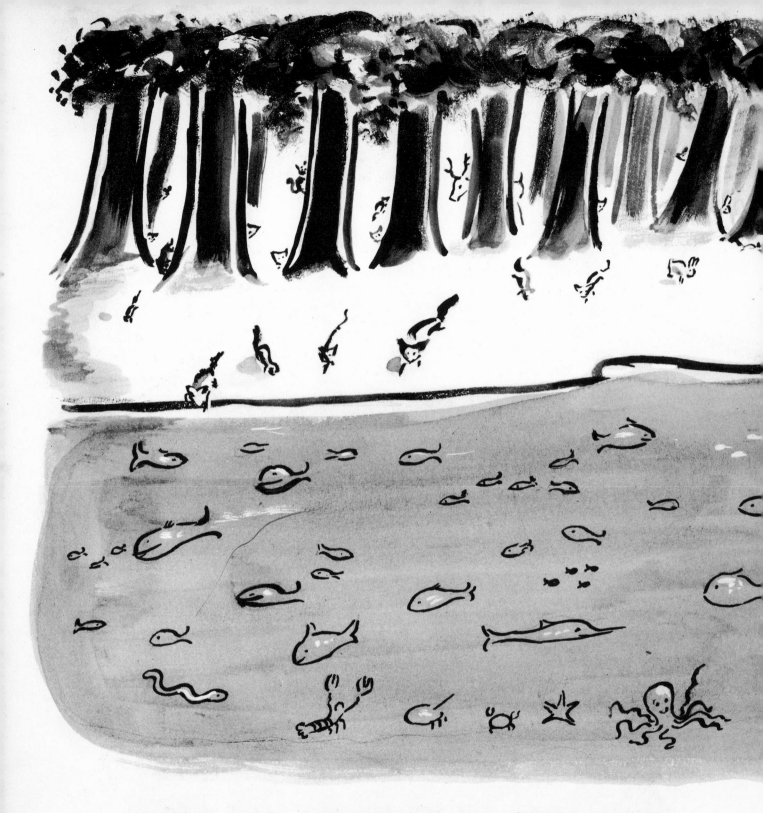

THERE ARE MILLIONS OF CREATURES
WHO LIVE IN THE WOODS

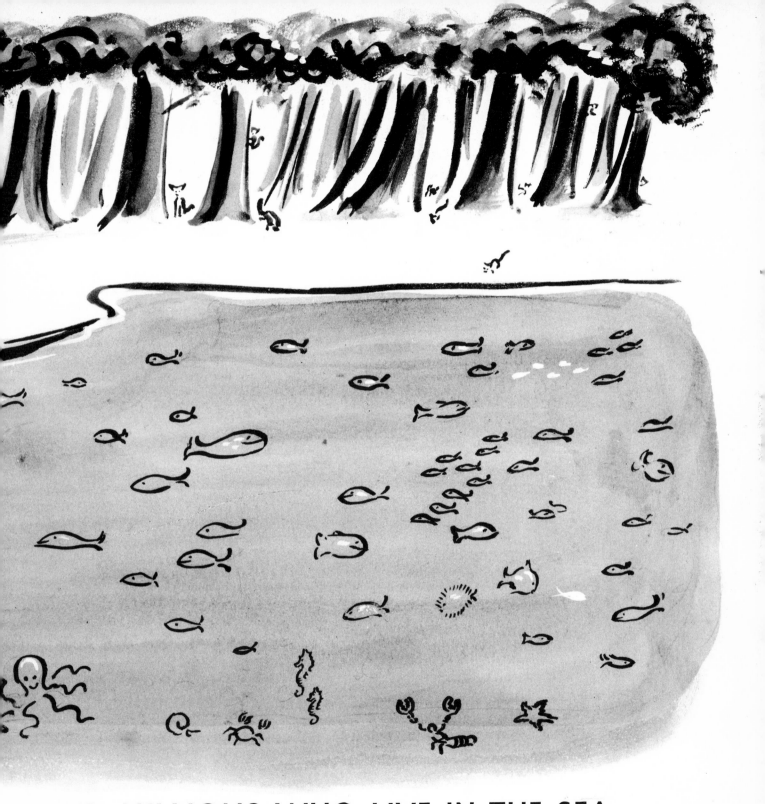

AND MILLIONS WHO LIVE IN THE SEA.

AND THERE ARE MILLIONS AND MILLIONS . . . .

BUT IN THE WHOLE WIDE WORLD

THERE IS ONLY ONE <u>YOU</u>
AND ONE <u>ME</u>.

THE END